Brad got Bob a big pig.

"What a big pig!" said the kids.

"It is grand!" brags Brad.

"Bob, you bat the pig."

"No! No!" said Bob.

"What if the pig pops?"

"You hit it!" said Brad.

"You can blast it till it pops."

4

"Who is the boss?" Bob said.

"Not you!"

"Blast it to bits!" said Brad.

"A split pig is grand!"

"What is in it?" asks Bob.

"Pop the pig, Bob!" said Brad.

Bob pops it and is glad!

The End